CW00430746

MR
EX LIBRIS

# J. SMITH

## A Fairy Story

by
Fougasse

MCMXXII

I

One night in mid-
September —
While storm-clouds
rode the air —
And a tempest swayed
the tree-tops —
Stripping the branches
bare —

A fairy was blown out of fairyland — and fell . . .

. . . in Eaton Square —

## II

The fairy looked
around him —
At a place he did
not know —
At the houses standing
straight & stiff —
And the lamp-posts
in a row —
And he couldn't guess
where he could be —
Nor yet which way
to go —

III

He blew up on his little hands —
He rubbed his little nose —

[He found it rather chilly —
In his little fairy clo'es] —

And clambered
up a lamp-post —
To warm his little
toes —

## IV

Then started off
to find his way —
back homewards,
if he could —

Or, failing that, some
clump of fern —

Or, possibly, a wood —
Whence he could get in touch once more — with his fairy brotherhood —

V

He trotted off...

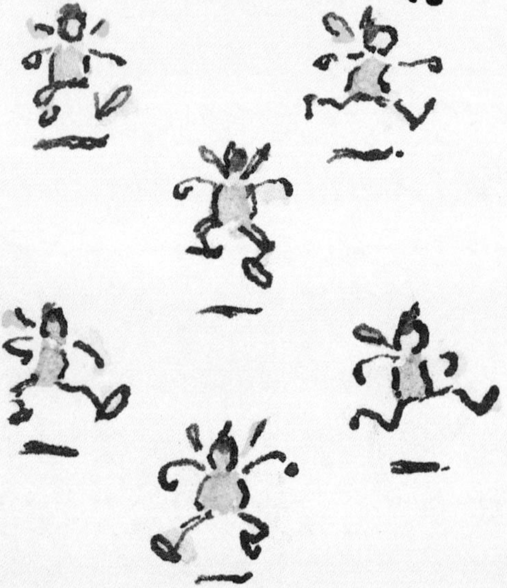

through Belgrave Place —

And up through
Belgrave Square —
Then all round
Wilton Crescent —
And back again
to where —
West Halkin leads
to Lowndes Street —
As doubtless you're
aware —

VI

Across Lowndes Square,
by William Street —
And on to Albert
Gate —

And there
he saw Hyde
Park in front —

Whereat his joy
was great —
For he thought it
was the country —
In all its natural
state —

# VII

The gate itself was
shut, of course —
Being after twelve
at night —
But that's
nothing to
a fairy —
And,
quicker
than I
can write —
He swung to the

top of the railings —
And . . .

. . . nearly fell
off in his fright —

## VIII

For a light flashed up
from the darkness —

And a sudden voice
said "Yes, —

I'm watching you,
young fellow, —
And I'll take your
name and address,
And just you come
along of me —
You and your
fancy-dress!" —

IX

The fairy blinked at
the light below—
In fear + trepidation,
And "Please," he said
"I've no address,—
Nor any designation."

"Very likely," said the constable — "We'll see about that at the station." —

# X

So sadly climbed
the fairy down —
And followed his
detector —
Through Basil Street
and Walton Street —
To the Depot
for that
Sector

And there he stood
before a desk —

With, behind it,
an Inspector —

XI
"Inspector,"
said the
constable —
"Patrolling, as I'm
used —
About the purlieus
of the Park, —

I came on the accused —
A-climbing over one of the gates —
— His name and address refused."

## XII

"Come, come," said
the Inspector —
"Now this will never
do, —
That's 'breaking-in',

And 'trespass', —
And 'forcing entry
through' —
What made you
act in such a way?
You're quite a
youngster too" —

CRIME
SHEET.

## XIII

"For such a crime
you must appear —
Before the Stipend-
iary —

Who, exercising, by the law —
His powers disciplinary —
Will put you for a season —
In the Penitentiary" —

"And when they lead you from the dock — And the Police-Court Missionary —" "Excuse me," said

the culprit —
"But I feel it's
necessary —
That I should first
explain that I —
Am only..." "What?"
"A fairy!" —

# XV

"A fairy?" said the
Inspector —
"A fairy?" he began
"Now that can surely
never be" —

He said, "It never can —
How can you be what don't exist,
You silly little man?" —

## XVI

"But they do exist,"
said the fairy —
"And the proof of
it is me — 
For if I'm
not a
fairy —
Whatever
can I
be? —

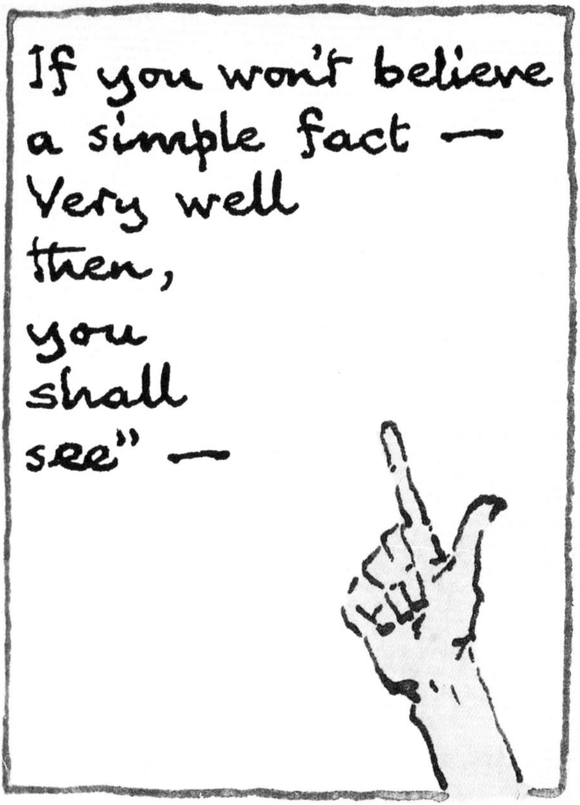

If you won't believe
a simple fact —
Very well
then,
you
shall
see" —

XVII

He stood
up on his
little toes —
And out his
arms he spread —
Then gently floated
through
the air —
And round
the
policeman's
head —

Then he . . .

. . . lay down
on the ceiling, and
"Well, p'raps you're
right," they said —

They locked him up

and down a bit,
And "Well, I'm
blessed," said one —
And "Same here,"
said the other —
"But what is to be
done?" —
There's nothing in
the bye-laws —
To deal with you,
my son!" —
??????????

# XIX

"If we take you to
the Magistrate —
He may not think
you real —

And talk about

'delusions' —
And 'misdirected
zeal' —
And suppose he
happened to be
right —
What asses
we should
feel!"

## XX

"Please, mister man,"
the fairy said —
"I did not mean to
trouble you —
I only

blew
here
by

mistake —

Like a
feather or
a bubble,
You — 
can tell me
where I am,
perhaps?" —

"London,"
they said,
"S.W." —

## XXI

"I only want to get back home —
I do not wish to stay —
The nearest wood will do for me —

Or any field of hay —

For there I'm sure to meet my friends — If you'll please to shew the way." —

XXII

"No field or wood,"
the Inspector said —
"Grows very near
this station —
The land about

is given up —
To human habit-
ation —
You could hardly
find," he said, "a less
congenial location" —

XXIII

"But if you'll bide
a bit with me —
And promise to be
good —
And not play any
fairy tricks,
And do
just what
you should,

On Thursday,

that's my
next day off —
We'll go and...

XXIV

So, when at length
the morning dawned,
And the Inspector's

work was done, —
He took the fairy
off with him —
To his home at
Number One —
Laburnum Grove,
where he put him
to bed —
With a glass of hot
milk + a bun —

## XXV

They woke next day,
and breakfasted —
And then, to shew
his gratitude —
The fairy danced
before his host —
With many a
curious attitude —

The Inspector
pronounced it "quite
fairy like" —
But of course that
was rather a
platitude —

XXVI

And then he asked him questions

of the fairies + their ways —

And what they did + thought about —

And how they
spent their days —
And if they'd shops
+ newspapers —

And
cinemas
and
plays —

## XXVII

"And, lastly, what
about yourself?" —
Said the Inspector
to his guest —
"What sort of job
can you perform?

What suits your fancy best? —
I liked that trick you did last night —
But tell me about the rest" —

XXVIII

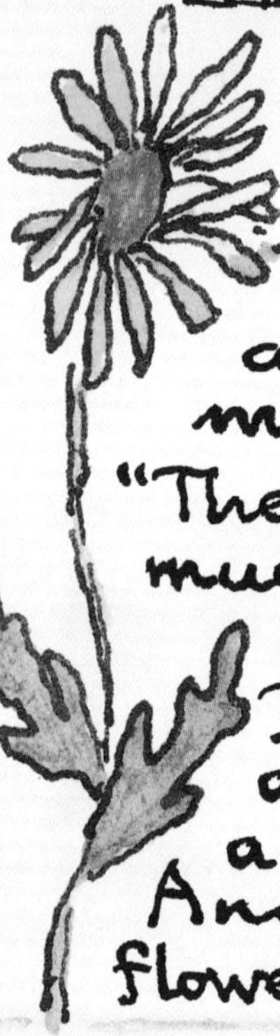

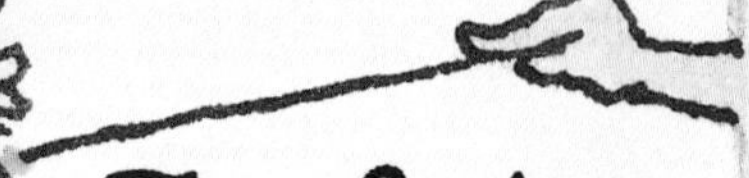

The fairy
answered
modestly—
"There isn't
much to
tell—
I can dance
a bit, + sing
a bit—
And paint a
flower or shell—

And I sometimes
help with the
sunsets —
But I cannot do
them well" —

XXIX

"In fact, I'm not
much of a fairy —
And many good
qualities lack —
At managing weather
I'm no good at all —

And of spells I have hardly the knack" — "If that's so," said his host, the Inspector — "Then why do you want to go back?" —

XXX
"Though you mayn't be great shakes as a fairy —
And only of lowly

degree —
And at most of
your fairy
employments —
Outclassed by the
others, maybe —
All the same, with
those tricks, as a
human, —
You'd soon
reach the
top of
the
tree" —

## XXXI

The fairy pondered
deeply —
And let his fancy
run —

He knew
he ought
to hurry
home —
But yet
... it
would
be fun! —

— And
vanity
wrestled
with
virtue,
Till,
finally,
vanity
won.

## XXXII

And so they sat
and settled —
The course on
which to go —

How the fairy
should pose as a
human boy —
of about ten years
or so —
As the nephew of
Inspector
Smith —
With
the
christian
name of
Joe —

XXXIII

'Twas thus they
laid their
programme,
and
thus
began
forthwith —
That most
astonishing career
Of the boy called
Joseph Smith —

Who started life
as a fairy —
Or, as some might
say, a myth —

XXXIV

He started off
by dancing —
At an amateur
affair —

In aid of the
Policemens'
Orphanage —
In a hall near
Vincent Square —
And never before
had the audience
seen —
Such dancing
anywhere —

XXXV

It created such amazement — that agents soon came round —

With promises of contracts —

And thus a job
he
found —
At the
Terpsichorean
Theatre,
[near
the
Aldwych
Under-
ground]

STAGE
DOOR

XXXVI
There
people flocked

To wonder at —
His marvellous
agility: —
He
did
the
most
surprising
feats —
With
effortless
facility —

And
on the
ground
or
in
the
air —
seemed
to
dance —
With
equal
ability —

XXXVII

And in the Press, they wrote of him —
In terms enthusiastic —

Of his 'rhythm', his
'kinetic grace' —
His 'poetry gym-
nastic', —
Employing all
the clever
words
from
'verve'
to 'light fantastic' —

XXXVIII

And invitations came so fast —

He . . .

Couldn't send
them answers —
From dukes
and
politicians

Down
to
'note-of-hand
advancers' —
From every
class
admirers came —
Save one ...

. . . his fellow-dancers!

XXXIX

But these weren't over-cordial —

If the truth must
be confessed —
And but little
admiration for —
His dancing they
expressed: —
In fact, they

called it
'amateur' —
And 'lacking
in
interest' —

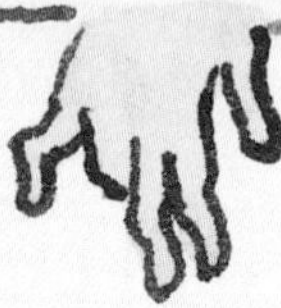

XL.

"He has
talent," they
admitted —
"And a
certain
sort of
style, —
But to call

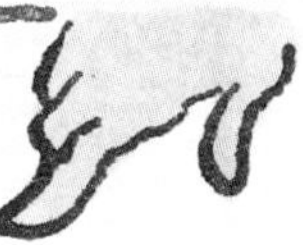

those antics
dancing...
Well, it
only makes
one smile; — 
And he's only
a child, +
what can he
know —
Of dancing
yet awhile?"

XLI

"He's only
a child,
and yet
he presumes
To try to
present on
the stage —
Dances
which take
many years

of hard work —
Why, it
cannot be
done at his
age!" —
And then they
would talk
of his lack
of technique —
Which drove
them quite
frantic with rage.

## XLII

"He calls it a dance of the fairies —
But we'd like to be told how he knows —
It's not quite what we were brought up to —

DANCING FOR BEGINNERS by

A MANUA OF DANCING BY AN EXPERT

DANCIN ILLUSTRATE

ICES NEW

And we do know a
bit, we suppose —
We've been taught
how to dance like
fairies for years —
And that's not at
all how it goes!" —

XLIII
They mocked
and they
scoffed and
derided —
And jeered
just as much
as they could.
At the 'second-
rate taste of
the public —
preferring
what's

new to what's
good' —
Till poor
sensitive
Joseph,
he
broke
down
+ wept —
At
being
so
misunderstood —

XLIV

"I'm sure
I don't
know what's
upset
them —
Or what I'm at
fault in," he
sighed —
"I thought that
as dancers they'd

surely approve —
Of the fairyland
dances I've tried —
But it certainly
seems that I'm
much in the
wrong —
Though it's
hard to
believe
it," he
cried —

XLV

"It's nice to be cheered and applauded —
And fêted

wherever I go —
The praise of
the public is all
very well —
But it's maybe
because they
don't know —
And if dancers
all say that I'm
no good at all —
Then I cannot
go on with the
show" —

STAGE DOOR
XLVI
So, having lost faith in his efforts —
He abandoned his dancing 'ere long

And turned his
attention to
music instead,
In which he
could hardly
go wrong —
For there's naught
like the magic
of fairyland
airs —
Or the charm of
a fairyland song.

XLVII

With pipes from
the rushes provided,

The same that
the fairies all
play —
He rendered the
music that runs
in the brooks —

And the
songs of the
wind in the
hay —
And the melodies
made by the sun,
and the dew, —
And the drone
of the bees on
the may —

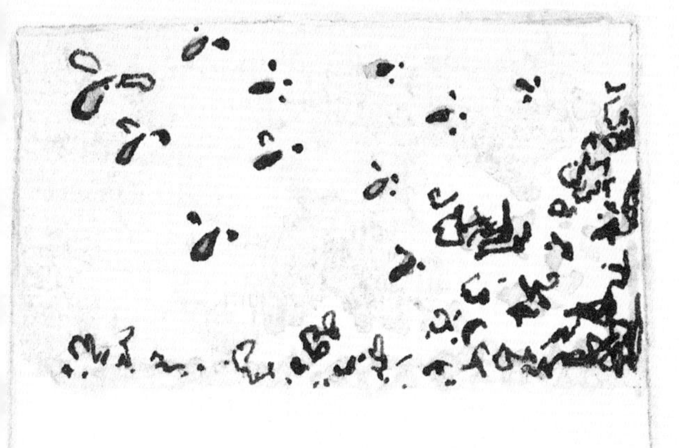

XLVIII

And songs did he
sing of the fairies —
And of life in the
fairy domains —

...Songs that they sing as they work & they play —
Songs of their pleasures and pains —
Cradle-songs,

spinning-songs,
songs of the
hunt —
And the warsongs
of fairy
campaigns —

XLIX

His concerts were packed to the ceiling —
And great the sensation he made —

With his delicate
singing, his strange
little songs —
And the exquisite
music he played —
And it soon was
agreed that his
musical skill —
Put his dancing
feats well in
the shade —

I

But again, I
am sorry
to tell
it —
Agreement
was not absolute —
The musical
experts
they quickly
began —

To discredit,
dispraise
+ dispute
And to
talk of
'the
immature
efforts —
Of this
prodigy
playing the
flute' —

## II

They heaped on
him scorn and
derision —
They told him he
knew not a thing —

Of harmony, counter-
point, thoroughbase—
Of tympani, wood-
wind, or string—
They said that his
melodies broke
all the laws—
And advised him
to learn how to
sing—

SINGING
MADE
EASY

How
to
Sing

The
SINGER
COM

LII
His music
recitals
went on for
a month —
During which
he had naught
but abuse —
From his
colleagues

inside the
profession —
Till finally
naught would
induce —
The unfortunate
fairy to stay in
a sphere —
Where the
experts
all thought
him no use —

He abandoned all
public appearance,
And decided to
follow instead —
The more peaceful

vocation of painter—
For "Here they can
hardly," he said—
"Call me ignorant
when, from my
earliest youth—
The life of a painter
I've led"—

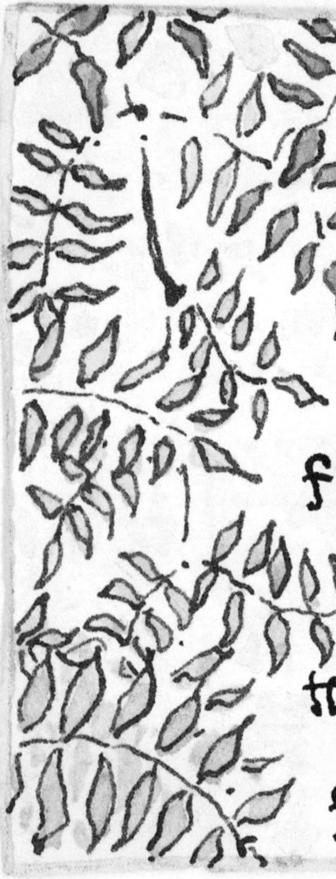

## LIV

"I've
many
years'
practice
at
colouring
flowers, —
And
at
tinting
the leaves
not a
few —

I've oftentimes painted the shells on the beach —

And rainbows...
I've worked on them
too —
And I've helped

with the dawns &
the sunsets —
Which is more than
a human can do" —

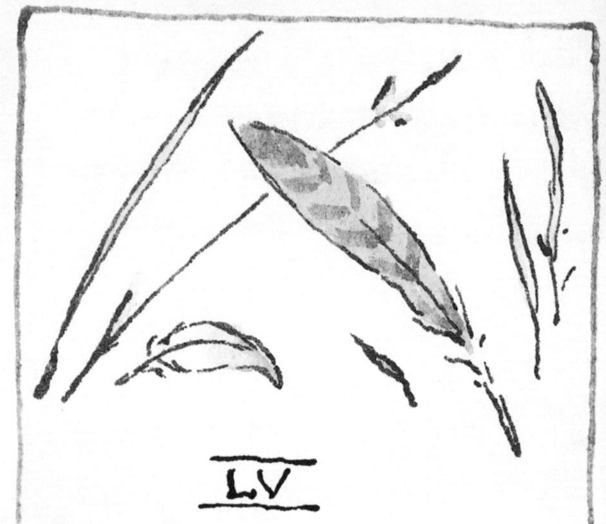

## LV

So with brushes of
feathers & grasses —
And colours that
come from the sun,
When his rays get

caught up in the
dewdrops —
The first fairy
painting's begun —
The daintiest
picture of blossom
in sunlight —
A wonderful work
when it's done —

## LVI

A marvel to those who beheld it —
So slight yet so calm +

complete —
The veriest soul
of the summer
it was —
Aglow with
its light +
its heat —
So
perfectly
peaceful
+ restful + soft —
In short, an
astonishing feat —

## LVII

And when it was
finished, he
framed it —
And off in a
taxi did go —

To the galleries
where a most
eminent guild
Were preparing
their annual
show—
Where he filled
up a form, and
presented his
work—
At the Secretary's
Office below—

## LVIII

And the eminent hanging committee —
Whose job is to

take or reject —
Met to settle the
fate of the pictures
sent in —
And had them
brought up to
inspect —

When they came to our hero's,
"Good Heavens" said one —
"What a very unpleasing effect!"

LIX
Said another,
"It's all out of drawing —
And those colours, they really appal,"

And a third said
"There's no com-
position" —
And a fourth said,
"There's nothing at
all!" —
And they chorussed

together "Oh, throw it outside, — We can't hang that stuff on the wall!" —

## IX

So the picture
returned to poor
Joseph —
With 'Rejected'
in chalk on the

back —
And he found
himself sadly
compelled to
confess —
That once more he
was on the wrong
track —
"It certainly seems,"
he admitted at
last —
"That there's
some human
virtue
I lack" —

LXI

"I cannot appeal
to the wise ones
at all —
It's only to those
who don't know —
What's the use of
going on with a
record like this, —
With nothing but
failure to shew? —
I'll get away back
to my people —
I wish I'd returned
long ago!" —

LXII

So he journeyed next day to the country —
And made his

way into
a
wood —
And
there he once more
donned his fairy
costume —
And slipped back
as fast as he could —
Into fairyland...
how, I can't tell
you —
Nor would it be
fair that I should —

LXIII

His friends & relations all welcomed him back —
And great

was their joy
to receive him —

[They were somewhat surprised at the story he told —
Though of course they were bound to believe him] —

And so, once again, he is safely at home —

And there we can happily leave him —

LXIV

But first we
must mention the
MORAL —
[In all the best
stories they do] —
It's an excellent
moral in every
way —
...In a sense, you
might say there
are two —
Both equally good;
What, exactly, they are

— Well, I think I can leave that to you!

THE

END

Published 2012 by Walker Books Ltd, 87 Vauxhall Walk, London SE11 5HJ
in association with Royal Collection Publications www.royalcollection.org.uk
Stable Yard House, St James's Palace, London SW1A 1JR

Based on an original work created by "Fougasse" (Cyril Kenneth Bird), and
preserved as part of the Library of The Queen's Dolls' House, Windsor Castle.



2 4 6 8 10 9 7 5 3 1

This book has been typeset in JSmith Printed in China 

British Library Cataloguing in Publication Data is available.
ISBN 978-1-4063-3793-8 www.walker.co.uk

# *About this book*

*J. Smith* by Fougasse is one of 200 miniature books created specially for Queen Mary's Dolls' House at Windsor Castle in 1922. The Dolls' House, the largest and most famous in the world, was created for Queen Mary, consort of King George V, by the renowned architect Sir Edwin Lutyens. It is a perfect replica of an aristocratic Edwardian residence complete with fully furnished rooms, electricity, running water and lifts.

*The Dolls' House under construction*

One of the most celebrated aspects of the house is the miniature library which still appears today as a remarkably balanced cross-section of the literary life of the period. It contains works by 171 authors, including Thomas Hardy, Rudyard Kipling, Sir Arthur Conan Doyle, Sir James Barrie and Edith Wharton.

The story of Joseph Smith is amongst the library's most enchanting and delightful volumes. It was the contribution of one of the foremost cartoonists of the day, "Fougasse" whose real name was Cyril Kenneth Bird. His witty illustrations for the "Careless Talk Costs Lives" posters were some of the most memorable images of World War II.

*J. Smith* is a work of true genius – in miniature. On pages no bigger than a postage stamp, Fougasse exquisitely hand-illustrated his magical story of a fairy lost in 1920s London. Reproduced here for the first time in their entirety, the tongue-in-cheek verse and charming illustrations remain an extraordinary delight to this day.